KITCHENER PUBLIC LIBRARY

3 9098 01792354 0

D0002931

Tell us what about Shojo Beat Manga!

available online. Go to:

shojobeat.com/mangasurvey

Skip·Beat!™

By Yoshiki Nakamura

Kyoko Mogami followed her true love Sho to Tokyo to support him while he made it big as an idol. But he's casting her out now that he's famous! Kyoko won't suffer in silence— she's going to get her sweet revenge by beating Sho in show biz!

Only $8⁹⁹

On sale at:
www.shojobeat.com
Also available at your local bookstore and comic store.

Skip·Beat! © Yoshiki Nakamura 2002/HAKUSENSHA, Inc.
Covers subject to change.

love ★ com

By Aya Nakahara

Lovely ★ Complex

Only $8⁹⁹

Risa Koizumi is the tallest girl in class, and the last thing she wants is the humiliation of standing next to Atsushi Ôtani, the shortest guy. Fate and the whole school have other ideas, and the two find themselves cast as the unwilling stars of a bizarre romantic comedy!

Shojo Beat
MANGA from the HEART

On sale at:
www.shojobeat.com
Also available at your local bookstore and comic store.

LOVE★COM © 2001 by Aya Nakahara/SHUEISHA Inc.

viz media
www.viz.com

Godchild™

By Kaori Yuki

Deep in the heart of 19th Century London, a young nobleman named Cain walks the shadowy cobblestone streets of the aristocratic society into which he was born. With Riff, his faithful manservant, Cain investigates his father's alleged involvement with a secret organization known as Delilah.

Shojo Beat Manga

Godchild

Kaori Yuki

Only $8⁹⁹

On sale at:
www.shojobeat.com

Also available at your local bookstore and comic store.

God Child © Kaori Yuki 2001/HAKUSENSHA, Inc.

RATED T+ FOR OLDER TEEN

viz media

www.viz.com

69

Story & Art by
Taeko Watanabe

Contents

Story Thus Far

It is the end of the Bakufu era, the 3rd year of Bunkyu (1863) in Kyoto. The Shinsengumi is a band of warriors formed to protect the Shogun.

Tominaga Sei, born as the daughter of a former Bakufu bushi, joined the Shinsengumi guised as a boy by the name of Kamiya Seizaburo to avenge her father and brother. She has continued her training under the only person in the Shinsengumi who knows her true identity, Okita Soji, and she aspires to become a true bushi.

Sei begins to develop feelings for Soji, who supports the Shinsengumi alongside the kind, compassionate and fervent Captain Kondo and the Vice Captain Hijikata. Sadly, Soji seems oblivious to her feelings.

When the Shinsengumi go up against their enemies at the Ikedaya Inn, Sei sees Okita fall in battle. She fights like a demon to defeat the enemy, and then fights like a doctor using her medical knowledge to keep Soji alive.

Characters

Tominaga Sei
She disguises herself as a boy to enter the Mibu-Roshi. She trains under Soji, aspiring to become a true bushi. But secretly, she is in love with Soji.

Okita Soji
Assistant vice captain of the Shinsengumi, and licensed master of the Ten'nen Rishin-Ryu. He supports the troop alongside Kondo and Hijikata and guides Seizaburo with a kind yet firm hand.

Kondo Isami
Captain of the Shinsengumi and fourth grandmaster of the Ten'nen Rishin-ryu. A passionate, warm and well-respected leader.

Hijikata Toshizo
Vice captain of the Shinsengumi. He commands both the group and himself with a rigid strictness. He is also known as the "Oni vice captain."

Yamanami Keisuke
Vice captain of the Shinsengumi. A master of the Hokushin Itto-Ryu, he is kind and well learned.

Akesato
A Shimabara prostitute who also knows Sei's true identity. She acts as Sei's "lover" to help disguise Sei's monthly feminine needs.

JUNE OF THE FIRST YEAR OF GENJI (1864).

A PUBLIC NOTICE WAS POSTED ON THE GOJO BRIDGE IN KYOTO BY THE SONJO-HA.

IT WAS UNDOUBTEDLY A ZANKAN-JO.*

The Shinsengumi is a guilty sinner in the Emperor's country. On a day not long from today, they will meet rightful retribution at the hand of God. Those faithful to Yoshio

IT CONDEMNED THE SHINSENGUMI FOR THE IKEDAYA ATTACK.

*A zankan-jo was a note that indicated the intent of killing a villain.

"KO"

KORENI KORIYO DOUSAIBOU

"LESSONS HARD TO LEARN ARE SWEET TO KNOW"

I told her it was business...

Onomi-chan's so harsh...

KYOTO "IROHA" KARUTA GAME

EVER SINCE THE IKEDAYA AFFAIR, I'VE REALLY ENJOYED WALKING AROUND TOWN, OKITA-SENSEI.

PAIR UP AND USE YOUR WHISTLE WHEN YOU NEED EXTRA HELP!

BUT KEEP IN MIND THAT WE DON'T KNOW WHEN THE SONJO-HA WILL RETALIATE, SO MAKE SURE YOU DON'T GET CAUGHT ALONE!

YES SIR!!

THE SHINSENGUMI PROTECTED THEM ALL FROM THE SONJO-HA'S ARSON.

IT MAKES ME FEEL PROUD.

THIS TOWN...

THESE PEOPLE...

OH NO! I FORGOT MY YATATE!*

I'M SORRY. I'LL BE RIGHT BACK.

OH, KAMIYA-SAN!

TRUE...

THAT INNKEEPER'S ALWAYS SO KIND.

...CHOSHU-SAMA TRIED TO KIDNAP THE EMPEROR BY LIGHTING THE IMPERIAL PALACE ON FIRE?

WHAT KIND OF IDIOT WOULD BELIEVE SUCH A STORY!

IT'S A BIG LIE THAT THE BAKUFU MADE UP TO JUSTIFY MERCILESSLY KILLING LOYAL SUPPORTERS OF THE EMPEROR WITH SUCH A LARGE BRUTAL FORCE!

BUT THEY SAY THE SHINSENGUMI WENT IN WITH ONLY FIVE...

...TO FIGHT A GROUP OF 20!

*A yatate was a portable writing utensil.

14

15

16

SO THERE ARE NO NATIVE BUSHI.

IT'S A CITY THAT FUNDAMENTALLY DISLIKES TROUBLE.

KYOTO'S THE CITY OF THE IMPERIAL PALACE.

ALL THE BUSHI AROUND HERE ARE FROM SOMEWHERE ELSE.

NO, I DON'T.

IT'S A FORM OF KINDNESS TO WANT TO AVOID CONFLICT EVEN IF IT MEANS LYING?

DON'T YOU THINK...

IT'S HARD FOR US TO UNDERSTAND BECAUSE THE PEOPLE OF EDO ARE SO QUICK TO FIGHT.

OH... WELL THEN...

...

20

YEAH! ONI-VICE-CAPTAIN REALLY NAILS IT SOMETIMES!!

I'M UP FOR THE CHALLENGE!

SETTLING THE SCORE FOR UENO-SAN AND KOSUGA-SAN!

I SWEAR ON THE HONOR OF THE SHINSENGUMI THAT I'LL FIND WHO DID THIS!!

WHERE'S THE CONFETTI COMING FROM?

THOUGH THE INTENTIONS WERE GOOD...

IT'S THE MIBU-RO! THE MIBU-RO!

AHHHH!

THEY'LL *EAT* YOU IF THEY CATCH YOU!

22

27

"THEN WHO WOULD YOU SAY YOU'RE FIGHTING FOR?"

I WASN'T PRAISED BY ANYONE...

...OR THANKED BY ANYONE.

IT WAS SIMPLY THE DAY I WAS PROUD OF BEING ABLE TO FOLLOW THROUGH WITH WHAT I BELIEVED TO BE TRUE.

AH...!

SQUEEZE ♡

I'M GOING TO WORK HARD!!

THANKS MABO!

KYA

WE'RE FIGHTING FOR OUR TRUTH!

THAT'S RIGHT.

IT'S NOT FOR ANYONE. I'M DOING IT FOR *ME*.

SENSEI'S DOING IT FOR HIMSELF.

30

OH NO! I'M SORRY.

T A P P

I THOUGHT I WOULD BRING HIM WITH ME WHILE WE'RE LOOKING FOR THE ASSASSIN...

YES, IT'S ACTUALLY UENO'S *DAITO*.*

Taking a break.

NO, NO. I'M SORRY, OKITA-SENSEI.

*Large katana.

UENO-SAN WAS USING A HAND SLOT STRING TOO?

BUT HE WAS SO LITTLE, HIS *DAITO* WAS TOO SHORT FOR ME...

SO INSTEAD I'M USING IT AS MY *SHOTO*.

YES, IT'S BECOME A TREND EVER SINCE THE IKEDAYA.

THAT'S A LONG *SHOTO*.*

*Small katana.

...

THAT'S RIGHT. KOSUGA-SAN HAD A HAND SLOT STRING ON HIS *DAITO*...

34

38

39

THE FAMED IKEDAYA AFFAIR FROM THE END OF THE BAKUFU ERA.

IT WAS AN INCIDENT THAT FOR BETTER OR WORSE MADE THE SHINSENGUMI KNOWN ALL OVER JAPAN AND CONFIRMED THE SONJO-HA'S ANTI-BAKUFU IDEOLOGY.

BUT THERE WAS ONE MAN WHO HAD NOTHING TO DO WITH THE INCIDENT, DESPITE BEING A TOP-RANKING OFFICIAL OF THE SHINSENGUMI.

OH!

WE ALREADY FINISHED THERE, VICE CAPTAIN YAMANAMI.

"E" え

EN NO SHITA NO CHIKARAMOCHI

"ONE CATCHES THE HARE AND ANOTHER EATS IT"

WHY AM I HERE?

WHY?

KYOTO "IROHA" KARU A GAME

YEAHHH!!

C'MON, KAMIYA! WE'RE GOING TO SHIMABARA!

WE JUST GOT A REWARD FROM THE AIZU CLAN FOR THE IKEDAYA AFFAIR!!

JU-JU-JUST OUT OF THE BLUE?!

10 RYO?!

EVERY MEMBER INVOLVED GOT 10 RYO* EACH!!

*By the way, their salary is 3 ryo a month.

42

44

46

*A sweets shop in Gion.

48

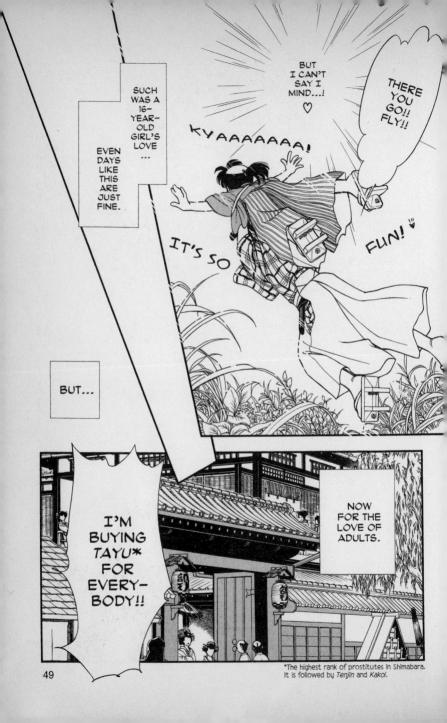

SUCH WAS A 16-YEAR-OLD GIRL'S LOVE ...

EVEN DAYS LIKE THIS ARE JUST FINE.

BUT I CAN'T SAY I MIND...! ♡

THERE YOU GO!! FLY!!

KYAAAAAAA!

IT'S SO

FUN!

BUT...

NOW FOR THE LOVE OF ADULTS.

I'M BUYING *TAYU** FOR EVERY-BODY!!

*The highest rank of prostitutes in Shimabara. It is followed by *Tenjin* and *Kakoi*.

49

50

51

52

53

54

55

56

Sign: "Responsible for Lord Matsudaira of Higo, Shinsengumi Residence"

57

60

61

64

I'LL GRATEFULLY ACCEPT THIS RYO!

YAMANAMI-SENSEI!!

BUT LET ME AT LEAST TREAT YOU TO SOME DRINKS!

NO ...

I MUST DECLINE.

I DON'T WANT KAMIYA-KUN TO BE UPSET WITH ME.

NO, BUT HE PROBABLY WOULDN'T FEEL COMFORT-ABLE IF HE KNEW.

GIGGLE

GIGGLE

OH, PLEASE.

SEIZABURO-HAN'S NOT THAT KIND OF MAN.

*A play on the Chinese characters used to spell Heisuke. "Sukebei" means pervert.

77

STING

"WORK."

GIGGLE GIGGLE

HE'LL WAIT FOR ME AT OUR REGULAR TEAHOUSE SO PLEASE STAY AS LONG AS YOU WANT.

KAMIYA-HAN'S WELL AWARE OF MY WORK.

N... NO...

KAMIYA-KUN'S BEEN ANXIOUSLY AWAITING THIS DAY FOR A MONTH.

RING ...

I'LL BE GOING NOW.

BABUMP

I'LL BE SEEING YOU THEN.

WH...

U...UM, YAMA-NAMI-SENSEI!

FOR MERCY'S SAKE!

I UNDER-STAND YOUR FEELINGS COMPLETELY BUT...

AKESATO-SAN...?

WON'T YOU STAY A WHILE LONGER?

*Normally the job requires the girls to be dispatched so clients aren't usually let upstairs. Of course there are exceptions to this rule.

80

82

HEH!

ALL THE SHIEIKAN MEMBERS COLLECTED EVERYTHING THEY HAD TO TAKE HIM OUT TO YOSHIWARA* FOR THE FIRST TIME...

THERE'S A HEROIC STORY ABOUT HIM FROM EDO.

HE REALLY IS A SUPER NICE GUY!

YOU LAUGH, BUT IT'S *TRUE!*

WHAT KIND OF VICE CAPTAIN WOULD MAKE A 16-YEAR-OLD GIRL WORRY ...

HEH HEH HEH

NICE! THAT'S WHAT WE LIKE TO HEAR!

WOBBLE WOBBLE

HAHA... HA... I COULDN'T GET A WINK OF SLEEP...

HE CAME BACK THE NEXT DAY WITH BLOOD-SHOT EYES...

YOU MAY LOOK SHY BUT APPARENTLY YOU'RE QUITE THE WOMANIZER!

WELL ...

CONGRATULATIONS ON YOUR YOSHIWARA DEBUT!!

*The Edo red light district where one needed official permission. There were many commoners who found it too exclusive and distanced themselves from it.

87

89 🌱 watering the plants for Sei.

92

94

95

97

98

IT'S BECAUSE UNLESS I TENSE UP MY FACE, I FEEL LIKE I'LL START LAUGHING.

AND... AND...

HUH? DOES IT LOOK THAT WAY?

ARE YOU UPSET ABOUT SOMETHING?

KAMIYA-SAN.

babump babump babump

"I'M HAPPY FOR YOU AND AKESATO-SAN." ♡

"HEEE HEEE, YAMANAMI-SENSEI, YOU DON'T HAVE TO HIDE ANYMORE."

I'M AFRAID I'LL SAY SOMETHING LIKE...

I got another mosquito bite.

Why do you sound so shady?

I JUST HAVE TO PRETEND LIKE I KNOW NOTHING ...

BUT IN ORDER FOR ME TO TAKE CARE OF MY MONTHLY BUSINESS AND STILL LET THEM BE TOGETHER...

IT LOOKS LIKE YOU'RE HAVING FUN.

THIS SUCKS !!

ALL I WANT TO DO IS CONGRATULATE HIM!!

SIGH

102

SHE MANAGED TO SHAVE A FEW YEARS OFF MY LIFE.

SHE CLAIMED SHE WAS CARRYING HIS CHILD SO SHE WOULDN'T BE SEPARATED FROM KAMIYA.

BUT DURING THE WHOLE KAMIYA ADOPTION THING...

HAVE YOU MET KAMIYA'S LOVER? HER NAME IS AKESATO.

AT FIRST SHE SEEMS LIKE A CLASSY, SHY BEAUTY...

GUILTY

HUH...

IT ENDED UP ALL BEING A SCAM.

BUT SHE HAD THE NERVE TO ASK ME TO END HER LIFE TO MAKE UP FOR HER DECEIT.

"I'M A BAD PERSON..."

THAT WAS IMPRESSIVE.

HA HA HA HA

KAMIYA'S A LUCKY GUY.

TO HAVE A GIRL LIKE THAT FALL HEAD OVER HEELS FOR HIM.

103

104

106

107

108

109

110

112

THE CHOSHU CLAN WAS PLANNING A RESURGENCE AND SECRETLY CONVENING SINCE THEY WERE CHASED OUT OF KYOTO AFTER THE AUGUST 18TH COUP OF THE PREVIOUS YEAR.

SUMMER OF THE FIRST YEAR OF GENGI (1864).

CHIRP CHIRP CHIRP

BUZZ BUZZ BUZZ

THEY TOOK ANOTHER BIG HIT BY LOSING MANY OF THEIR KEY FIGURES ON JUNE 5TH OF THIS YEAR AT THE IKEDAYA AFFAIR AT THE HANDS OF THE SHINSENGUMI.

池田屋

HOW-EVER...

"A" あ

ASHIMOTO KARA TORI GA TATSU "PROTECT YOURSELF AT ALL POINTS"

KYOTO "IROHA" KARU A GAME

(lit. A bird emerges from under one's feet.)

SHAVING ONE'S HEAD IS A FORM OF NON-JUDICIAL PUNISHMENT FOR A GIRL.

BUT THERE IS!

I CAN'T BELIEVE THAT THERE'S ANYONE WHO WOULD ENDURE SUCH SHAME OTHER THAN TO BECOME A NUN!

OSEI-CHAN IS THAT KIND OF GIRL!

BUT IF THAT'S THE CASE...

WHY DID KAMIYA-KUN STAY AFTER AVENGING HER FAMILY?

BECAUSE...

SHE FOUND SOMETHING IN THE SHINSENGUMI...

...THAT SHE WOULD GIVE HER LIFE FOR... I THINK.

YOU...!

YES?

I COULD NEVER TELL HIM AKESATO TOLD ME EVERY-THING...

SHE ONLY TOLD ME BECAUSE SHE TRUSTED I WOULD NEVER MENTION IT TO ANYBODY.

I MEAN ...

THE NEXT BATTLE SEEMS TO BE A BIG ONE.

BABUMP

BABUMP

BABUMP

"BUT YOU STILL WANT KAMIYA-KUN TO GO?

YES.

"YOU WOULD KNOWINGLY LEAD A GIRL TO THE BATTLEFIELD."

SPIN

SO...?!

121

UH... UPP...

THAT MEANS I CAN PREVENT KAMIYA-KUN FROM HAVING TO GO TO BATTLE AS LONG AS I'M SICK!

!!

WHAT?! C'MON, OKITA-SENSEI!!

SPINNING

OH, I'M DIZZY...

NO...NO, IT'S NOTHING. YOU SHOULD GO WITH EVERYONE...

YAMA-NAMI-SENSEI?!

I CAN'T LEAVE YOU LOOKING LIKE THIS!

WELL THEN, KAMIYA-KUN!

TAKE GOOD CARE OF VICE CAPTAIN YAMANAMI!

DON'T WORRY, KAMIYA-SAN!

I'LL MAKE SURE AND PROTECT CAPTAIN KONDO!

Seizaburo's lioness pose!

SHE'S PROBABLY GOING TO DEVELOP INTO MORE OF A WOMAN...

IT'S A MIRACLE SHE WENT UNHARMED AMONGST THOSE ANIMALS.

AND HOW DELICATE HER BODY IS!

IT'S PROBABLY JUST ME, BUT THE CLOTH AROUND HER CHEST LOOKS SO SULTRY.

WHAT IS SHE GOING TO DO?! SHE WON'T BE ABLE TO DECEIVE THEM FOREVER!!

A millennium treat from the author ?!

OH... THANK YOU.

I'M SURE YOU WANT TO JOIN THE REST AT THE FRONT LINE AS WELL!

I'LL AT LEAST GET YOU PREPARED FOR BATTLE.

I CAN'T BELIEVE HOW HEAVY CHAIN MAIL IS!*

WOW!

CLANK

*They usually weighed over 5 kg. It was over 10 kg with the rest of the armor.

126

...CHOOSE THE PATH OF A BUSHI WITH SUCH DEDICATION?

...YES?

WHY WOULD A GIRL...

YOU...

IT MUST BE ABOUT AKESATO-SAN!

URRR! HE DOESN'T HAVE TO HIDE IT!

TICKLE

TICKLE

NO...

I'M SORRY, IT'S NOTHING.

I can't ask her that.

CHOSHU SAGA TROOPS

NIJO CASTLE

KINRI IMPERIAL PALACE

SHINSEN-GUMI HEAD-QUARTERS

SENBON-DORI

SHIJO-DORI

KATSURA RIVER

KAMO RIVER

NISHIKOKU-KAIDO

ZENITORI BRIDGE

HERE!!

FUSHIMI-KAIDO

OMITTED IN BETWEEN

TAKEDA-KAIDO

CHOSHU YAMAZAKI TROOPS

CHOSHU FUSHIMI TROOPS

UJI RIVER

MEANWHILE, THE SHINSENGUMI WERE STAKED OUT WITH THE AIZU TROOPS FROM THE TAKEDA-KAIDO TO THE KUJO RIVERSIDE AND THE ZENITORI BRIDGE AREA.

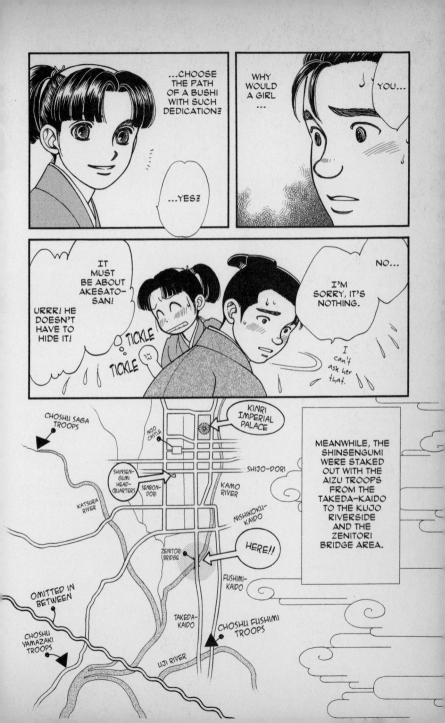

*He would be the 15th shogun, Tokugawa Yoshinobu. He was given his nickname from being the family head of the Hitotsubashi family and eating a lot of pork which was considered disgusting by the common folk. His household of the Mito-Tokugawa was also the lineage of "Mito-gaku" which was the predecessor of Sonjo ideology.

131

THE FACT THAT THEY REFUSED TO WITHDRAW WHEN ORDERED BY THE BAKUFU IS REASON ENOUGH FOR US TO LAUNCH AN ATTACK!!

NO WAY!!

THE CHOSHU TROOPS ARE RIGHT THERE!

EVEN IF THEY COME INTO POWER, IT'LL BE A CLEAN OUT FOR HIM SO LONG AS HE CAN SAY THEY DISOBEYED A DIRECT ORDER FROM THE IMPERIAL COURT NOT TO INVADE KYOTO.

WHAT ?!

HE'S WAITING FOR THE CHOSHU TO INVADE KYOTO.

WHY DOESN'T HE ORDER US TO MOVE IN?!

HOW CAN WE FIGHT LIKE BUSHI WITH A LEADER LIKE THAT?!

HE'S NOT WORRIED ABOUT WINNING THIS BATTLE... HE JUST WANTS TO SECURE A WAY OUT.

136

138

WE'LL BE STEPPING ON THE AIZU CLAN'S FEET TOO.

I'M SURE THEY'D LISTEN TO AN ORDER FROM KATAMORI-SAMA.

PLEASE FURTHER THE TALKS AND PUT A STOP TO THIS!!

I WONDER WHY I TOLD OKITA-SAN...

...THAT I WAS AN AIZU LOYALIST...

AND ...

YEAHHH!!

GALLOP GALLOP GALLOP

Hey! Let us in!

THE RECKLESS DEED OF THE SHINSENGUMI TRYING TO BREAK INTO YOSHINOBU'S QUARTERS IN A BLAZE OF TEMPER ...

...WAS DISMISSED THANKS TO AIZU KATAMORI, BUT STILL...

139

140

142

I WON'T ASK WHO THE OBJECT OF HER AFFECTION IS.

...KAMIYA-KUN.

WELL NOW...

I FEEL LIKE I UNDERSTAND A LITTLE...

YAMANAMI-SENSEI...!

THIS IS AN ORDER FROM YOUR VICE CAPTAIN.

YOU'LL JOIN THE REST AT THE KUJO RIVERSIDE TOMORROW.

BUT ON ONE CONDITION...

144

THANK YOU VERY MUCH!!

KAMIYA SEIZABURO...

...WILL NEVER FORGET THIS FEELING OF GRATITUDE!!

NO, NO. YOU SHOULD FORGET. ♡

DAMN

TELL SOJI I SAID HELLO!

FEELING LIKE HE PAID OFF A HUGE DEBT.

He...he totally knows?!

WE'VE BEEN ORDERED TO TAKE THE FIELD!!

GONG GONG

WE'RE TAKING THE FIELD!!

AS FATE WOULD HAVE IT...

THE CHOSHU TROOPS ENTERED THE FORBIDDEN KYOTO THAT SAME EARLY MORNING.

145

146

OKITA-SENSEI!!

...!

"SA" さ

SAO NO SAKI NI SUZU "WITH VOLLIES OF ETERNAL BABBLE"

(lit. A bell on the end of a rod)

KYOTO "IROHA" KARUTA GAME

150

152

YEAHHHH!!

SHIN-SENGUMI! CHARGE!!

ABOUT THIS TIME...

THE CHOSHU TROOPS CAMPED OUT IN FUSHIMI BEGAN BATTLE WITH THE BAKUFU AND ŌGAKI TROOPS JUST EAST OF THE KUJO RIVERSIDE, AT FUJINOMORI.

THE SHIN-SENGUMI CAME TO ASSIST THE ŌGAKI TROOPS ALONGSIDE THE AIZU CLAN.

KAMIYA-SAN!

YES!

154

THERE'S AN URGENT MESSAGE FROM THE AIZU TROOPS GUARDING THE HAMAGURI GATES OF THE IMPERIAL PALACE!

WHAT?!

I CAN SEE SMOKE AS WELL!!

GUNSHOT IN THE DIRECTION OF THE IMPERIAL PALACE!!

WHAT'S THAT SOUND?

WHAT?!

"LEAVE FUSHIMI AND GO TO THE IMPERIAL PALACE IMMEDIATELY!

"THE KINRI IS CURRENTLY UNDER FIERCE ATTACK BY THE CHOSHU TROOPS!"

YOU'RE SAYING THEY FIRED ON THE EMPEROR!

THOSE SUPPOSEDLY LOYAL TO HIM?!

158

IN THAT SENSE, IT CAN BE SAID THAT KATSURA REPRESENTED A "NEW BREED" WITH A MODERN SENSE OF PRESENT-DAY SOCIETY.

Sort of like this?

IT'S NO WONDER HE WAS AT ODDS WITH THE SHINSENGUMI (HEH).

WHAT'S WRONG WITH RESPECTING THE OLD BUSHI WAYS ?!

THAT'S RIGHT! IT'S BECAUSE WE'RE FARMERS!

BUT THAT IS A DISCUSSION FOR ANOTHER TIME...

OUR STORY RETURNS TO THE "KINMON NO HEN."

BANG!

BANG!

BANG!

BANG!

THE CHOSHU RESIDENCE HAS BURST INTO FLAMES!!

IT SEEMS THAT THE CHOSHU SET THE FIRE THEMSELVES WHEN FLEEING!

THEY WANT TO DESTROY ANY PROOF OF INSURGENCE!

WHAT INCONSIDERATE BASTARDS.

THE WIND'S PICKING UP.

I HOPE THIS DOESN'T SPREAD INTO TOWN...

KAMIYA-SAN!

YES! I'M STILL ALIVE!!

SEI'S WISH WOULD BE BETRAYED IN THE MOST ILL-FATED WAY...

162

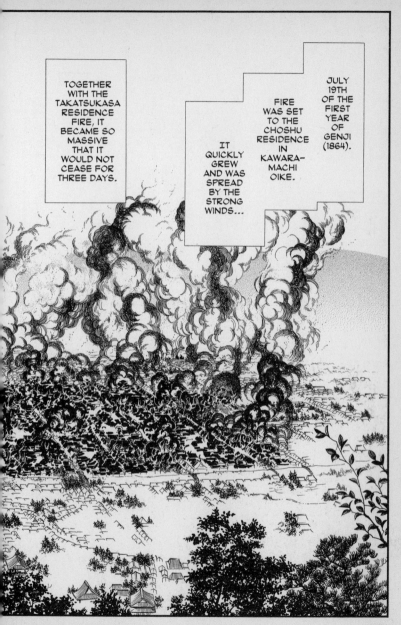

TOGETHER WITH THE TAKATSUKASA RESIDENCE FIRE, IT BECAME SO MASSIVE THAT IT WOULD NOT CEASE FOR THREE DAYS.

IT QUICKLY GREW AND WAS SPREAD BY THE STRONG WINDS...

FIRE WAS SET TO THE CHOSHU RESIDENCE IN KAWARA-MACHI OIKE.

JULY 19TH OF THE FIRST YEAR OF GENJI (1864).

THE FIRE WAS CALLED "BANG BANG FIRE" BY THE PEOPLE, DRAWING FROM THE SOUND OF GUNSHOT.

APPROXI-MATELY 2,800 HOMES FELL TO THE FIRE.

THE FOLLOWING DAY ON THE 20TH, IT WOULD UNRAVEL AS AN EVEN BIGGER TRAGEDY.

RAKUSEI, MIBU VILLAGE

SHIN-SENGUMI HEAD-QUARTERS

IT DOESN'T LOOK GOOD YAMANAMI-SAN!

THAT FIRE MIGHT CROSS HORI RIVER AND REACH HERE.

IF THERE'S A SAFE PLACE FOR THE ELDERS AND THE CHILDREN, THEY SHOULD GO THERE NOW.

IT WOULD PROBABLY BE BEST TO PREPARE FOR THE WORST.

IS IT NOT SAFE HERE?

TAMEBO... YUBO...

AREN'T THEY IN TOWN?

ARE OKITA-HAN AND KAMIYA-HAN ALL RIGHT?

They can be so damn cute.

IT'S ALL RIGHT.

THEY'RE NOT THE KIND OF GUYS THAT DIE THAT EASILY.

*A prison located in Rokkaku-Shinsenen and only about 600 m from the Shinsengumi headquarters.

*Something that made it obvious if one was a friend or foe during battle.

168

170

171

172

ABSOLVE THEM TEMPORARILY* AND THEY HAVE NO REASON TO RETURN!

THEY'RE ALL ENEMIES OF THE STATE!!

THEY HAVEN'T EVEN BEEN INVESTIGATED YET!

WHAT RIGHT DO YOU HAVE TO ACT SO CRUELLY?!

WE HAD NO CHOICE...!

WHY DON'T YOU ACT ON YOUR FEELINGS THEN?!

I WOULDN'T FEEL SO TORMENTED IF IT WEREN'T FOR THAT!

YOU'RE OUT OF LINE!

DO YOU

...HAVE NO SOLDIER'S MERCY?!

BANG

*When a prison was on fire, all prisoners except for death row inmates and major criminals were temporarily absolved as long as they returned to a specified location within three days on condition that their charges would be reduced. However, if they broke their promise, they would be put to death.

177

178

To Be Continued!

THIS IS FOR THOSE NORMAL SHOJO MANGA READERS WHO MAY NOT BE SO FAMILIAR WITH JAPANESE HISTORY OR THE SHINSENGUMI (HEH).

SO THIS IS HOW "KAZE HIKARU DIARY R" WAS RESURRECTED, AND IT'LL BE THE SAME AS BEFORE.

BACK-TO-THE-BASICS... I'M GOING TO TELL YOU ONE OF KAZE HIKARU'S PRODUCTION SECRETS.

SEI-CHAN WAS ACTUALLY ALMOST NOT ABLE TO JOIN THE SHINESENGUMI!

SUCH IS THE SECRET!

HUH? WHY NOT?

YOUR PERIOD!!

WHO CARES? JUST TRICK THE READERS WITH THE "SHOJO MANGA RULE" LIKE ALWAYS.

WHAT THE HELL ARE YOU GOING TO DO? IT'S A LITTLE MORE COMPLICATED THAN BATHING OR GOING TO THE BATHROOM!

I CAN'T !!

I DO SOMETHING THAT SILLY HERE, AND SEI-CHAN'S EXISTENCE WILL LOSE ALL CREDIBILITY!

I'll also lose the readers' empathy.

186

HOW AM I SUPPOSED TO PROTECT OKITA-SENSEI?

NO WAY!!

IF I CAN'T GET AROUND THIS, I MIGHT HAVE TO GIVE UP ON THE "HEROINE JOINING THE SHINSENGUMI" SCENARIO!!

I can't even be a bushi?

I WAS A LIGHT ONE, SO I COULD EVEN ATTEND P.E. CLASSES LIKE THAT.

I EVEN INTER-VIEWED MY ASSIS-TANT'S GRAND-MOTHER.

WOW!

OH, GOODNESS. I HAVEN'T SEEN YOU FOR AWHILE AND THE QUESTIONS YOU COME UP WITH...

DO YOU KNOW WHAT YOUR GRANDMA DID?

I INTER-VIEWED MY GRAND-MOTHER IN A DESPER-ATE ATTEMPT.

It's got to be close to the end of the Bakufu era...

I'VE DEVELOPED A WHOLE NEW RESPECT FOR THEIR SENSE OF DIGNITY.

HE HE

HE HE

THEY WERE POETS WHO COULD ALSO SING AND WRITE.

HOW VALIANT THOSE MEIJI WOMEN WERE ...

THE AUTHOR FOUND NEW APPRECIATION FOR THE ELDERLY.

BUT OF COURSE I COULDN'T FIND OUT ABOUT THE END OF THE BAKUFU ERA...

THAT'S RIGHT! A "WOMAN"!

WAIT A SEC!

187

I FOUND IT!

THEY CALLED IT "GYOUZUI"?!

AND...

THERE MIGHT BE SOMETHING WRITTEN ABOUT PERIODS FROM THE POINT OF VIEW OF A GEISHA!

THERE WAS SO MUCH WRITTEN ABOUT GEISHAS!!

• Gyouzui?

THEY ONLY GOT TWO DAYS OFF?!

THERE'S GOT TO BE AN ILLUSTRATION SOMEWHERE!

A PICTURE! SHOW ME A PICTURE!

SO WHAT WAS A "HORSE" MADE OF?! WHAT SHAPE WAS IT?!

SO BEGAN THE DAYS I WAS BURIED IN GEISHA-RELATED DOCUMENTS.

SEE...I KNEW IT! EVEN IF YOU BOUGHT A GEISHA, IT DIDN'T NECESSARILY MEAN YOU'D GET ANY!

AND I BECAME SORT OF AN EXPERT IN THAT WORLD (HEH).

What are you reading?

I KNEW SOJI WOULDN'T SCREW AROUND WITH THEM.

HE HE HE HE.

I THOUGHT YOU WERE RESEARCHING THE "HORSE"!

GEISHA ENCYCLOPEDIA

ASSISTANT

188

Kaze Hikaru Diary R: The End

Decoding Kaze Hikaru

Kaze Hikaru is a historical drama based in 19th century Japan and thus contains some fairly mystifying terminology. In this glossary we'll break down archaic phrases, terms, and other linguistic curiosities for you, so that you can move through life with the smug assurance that you are indeed a know-it-all.

First and foremost, because *Kaze Hikaru* is a period story, we kept all character names in their traditional Japanese form—that is, family name followed by first name. For example, the character Okita Soji's family name is Okita and his personal name is Soji.

AKO-ROSHI:
The ronin (samurai) of Ako; featured in the immortal Kabuki play *Chushingura* (Loyalty), aka *47 Samurai*.

ANI-UE:
Literally, "brother above"; an honorific for an elder male sibling.

BAKUFU:
Literally, "tent government." Shogunate; the feudal, military government that dominated Japan for more than 200 years.

BUSHI:
A samurai or warrior (part of the compound word *bushido*, which means "way of the warrior").

CHICHI-UE:
An honorific suffix meaning "father above."

DO:
In kendo (a Japanese fencing sport that uses bamboo swords), a short way of describing the offensive single-hit strike *shikake waza ippon uchi*.

-HAN:

The same as the honorific –SAN, pronounced in the dialect of southern Japan.

-KUN:

An honorific suffix that indicates a difference in rank and title. The use of *kun* is also a way of indicating familiarity and friendliness between students or compatriots.

MEN:

In the context of *Kaze Hikaru*, *men* refers to one of the "points" in kendo. It is a strike to the forehead and is considered a basic move.

MIBU-ROSHI:

A group of warriors that supports the Bakufu.

NE'E-SAN:

Can mean "older sister," "ma'am," or "miss."

NI'I-CHAN:

Short for *oni'i-san* or *oni'i-chan*, meaning older brother.

OKU-SAMA:

This is a polite way to refer to someone's wife. *Oku* means "deep" or "further back," and comes from the fact that wives (in affluent families) stayed hidden away in the back rooms of the house.

ONI:

Literally "ogre," this is Sei's nickname for Vice-Captain Hijikata.

RANPO:

Medical science derived from the Dutch.

RONIN:

Masterless samurai.

RYO:

At the time, one *ryo* and two *bu* (four bu equaled roughly one ryo) were enough currency to support a family of five for an entire month.

-SAN:

An honorific suffix that carries the meaning of "Mr." or "Ms."

SENSEI:

A teacher, master, or instructor.

SEPPUKU:

A ritualistic suicide that was considered a privilege of the nobility and samurai elite.

SONJO-HA:

Those loyal to the emperor and dedicated to the expulsion of foreigners from the country.

TAMEBO:

A short version of the name Tamesaburo.

YUBO:

A short version of the name Yunosuke.

I experimented a little with this volume's cover (*laugh*). I like illustrations where you can't actually see the character's face because it tickles your imagination to think about what kind of expression they have. That's probably why I have so many scenes in my manga where you can't see the character's entire face. Having said that, I can also see that it's frustrating to a reader to wonder "why don't they look this way?" Sorry that the author is so pigheaded (*laugh*). To make up for it, I had Sei-chan grab Soji's uniform.

Taeko Watanabe debuted as a manga artist in 1979 with her story *Waka-chan no Netsuai Jidai* (Love Struck Days of Waka). *Kaze Hikaru* is her longest-running series, but she has created a number of other popular series. Watanabe is a two-time winner of the prestigious Shogakukan Manga Award in the girls category—her manga *Hajime-chan ga Ichiban!* (Hajime-chan Is Number One!) claimed the award in 1991 and *Kaze Hikaru* took it in 2003.

Watanabe read hundreds of historical sources to create *Kaze Hikaru*. She is from Tokyo.

KAZE HIKARU VOL. 7
The Shojo Beat Manga Edition

STORY AND ART BY
TAEKO WATANABE

Translation & English Adaptation/Mai Ihara
Touch-up Art & Lettering/Rina Mapa
Design/Izumi Evers
Editor/Jonathan Tarbox

Editor in Chief, Books/Alvin Lu
Editor in Chief, Magazines/Marc Weidenbaum
VP of Publishing Licensing/Rika Inouye
VP of Sales/Gonzalo Ferreyra
Sr. VP of Marketing/Liza Coppola
Publisher/Hyoe Narita

© 2000 Taeko WATANABE/Shogakukan Inc. First published by Shogakukan Inc. in
Japan as "Kaze Hikaru." All rights reserved. The stories, characters and incidents mentioned
in this publication are entirely fictional.

No portion of this book may be reproduced or transmitted in any form or by any means
without written permission from the copyright holders.

Printed in Canada

Published by VIZ Media, LLC
P.O. Box 77010
San Francisco, CA 94107

Shojo Beat Manga Edition
10 9 8 7 6 5 4 3 2 1
First printing, November 2007

www.viz.com

PARENTAL ADVISORY
KAZE HIKARU is rated T+ for Older Teen and is
recommended for ages 16 and up. This volume
contains realistic violence, alcohol use, and sexual
themes.
ratings.viz.com

store.viz.com